G000067419

VIKING
MYTHS & LEGENDS

by John Snelling

Illustrated by Margaret Theakston

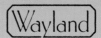

ℳYTHS AND ℒEGENDS

Celtic Myths and Legends
Greek Myths and Legends
Roman Myths and Legends
Viking Myths and Legends

Editor: Jillie Norrey
Designed by: DP Press, Sevenoaks, Kent
Consultant: Dr Dominic Tweddle (York
Archaeological Trust)

First published in 1987 by
Wayland (Publishers) Ltd,
61 Western Road, Hove
East Sussex, BN3 1JD, England

British Library Cataloguing in Publication Data
Snelling, John, *1943–*
    Viking myths and legends. – (Myths and
    legends).
    1. Mythology, Norse – Juvenile literature
    I. Title   II. Theakston, Margaret
    III. Series
    293′.13   BL860

ISBN 1 85210 231 4

Phototypeset by Kalligraphics Ltd, Redhill, Surrey
Printed by G. Canale & C.S.p.A., Turin
Bound in Britain at The Bath Press, Avon

Contents

Introduction

The Vikings were a tough, restless people from the Scandinavian countries – Norway, Sweden and Denmark. The bite of frost and winter wind, the pangs of hunger and the dark of long winter nights all helped to forge their steel-hard spirit. Life for them was a kind of fight – and fighting was what they were best at. Their long ships travelled all over Europe, raiding and plundering wherever they went. Sometimes, however, they would settle down in one place. Then they became farmers, fishermen and traders. Later, when they became Christians, they gave up their old bloodthirsty ways altogether.

The Viking poets told marvellous stories during the long winter evenings. Sometimes these stories would have been about the gods that lived in a kingdom called Asgard. The greatest of them was Odin. He was mighty in battle – but he was also wise. Odin had two halls: Valaskjalf and Valhalla. Thor, Freyr, and Balder were other great gods. There were goddesses too: Frigg, Freyja, Idun and Sif.

Bifrost, the rainbow bridge, joined Asgard to another realm called Midgard. People lived on Midgard, and a wall protected them from giants and ogres. The Vikings also believed in dwarfs and elves. Below Midgard there was a dark and dreadful realm called Niflheim. Hel, the Kingdom of the Dead, was situated here.

At the centre of the world towered a great ash tree called Yggdrasill. An eagle perched on the topmost branch. At the root slithered a huge snake. The eagle and the snake were always at war. A squirrel ran up and down the tree carrying insults between them.

The Wall of Asgard

While the gods were building Asgard, a stranger appeared. 'You need a wall to protect your kingdom from giants and ogres,' he told them. 'Let me build one for you. I could do the work within eighteen months.'

The gods liked the idea. 'But what would be your price?' they wanted to know.

'That the goddess Freyja becomes my wife,' the builder replied; 'and that you give me the sun and the moon as well.'

11

The gods went away and talked it over. They all thought that the price was too high. 'We'll just have to say no,' they said.

'Wait a minute,' said Loki, who enjoyed making trouble. Mischief Maker, Trickster and Shape Changer were Loki's other names. 'We could agree to the giant's price, but we could tell him that he would have to finish the work in a single winter. That's just six months. If he took a day longer, he'd have to go away without his wages.'

'He'd be a fool to agree to that,' the gods said.

'But there's no harm in trying,' replied Loki.

13

When he heard Loki's terms, the builder glared and became very silent. Then he muttered, 'It's a very hard bargain — but I accept it. However, I will need to use my horse, Svadilfari.'

The builder began work on the first day of winter. He worked hard, but Svadilfari worked even harder hauling great loads of huge stones. The wall went up amazingly quickly.

By the time summer was just three days away, only the gate-house remained unfinished. That made the gods very worried. They began to look for someone to blame.

'*Loki!*' they all cried, turning on the Trickster and seizing him. 'You got us into this mess, so you can get us out of it.'

'All right, all right!' cried Loki. 'I'll find a way, *I promise*.'

15

That evening the builder took Svadilfari out to fetch the last load of stones. Suddenly a beautiful white mare appeared. She whinnied to Svadilfari, who at once lost his heart – and his head. He broke his harness and ran after the mare. *'Hey, stop!'* cried the builder. But it was no use. Svadilfari and the mare vanished into the woods.

Now the builder knew that there was no chance at all of finishing his work on time. 'I've been tricked!' he cried angrily and stormed off to see the gods.

Thor paid the builder his wages. He did not give him Freyja, nor the sun and the moon. Instead he gave him a blow on the head. The builder's skull was shattered into thousands of tiny pieces.

When Loki appeared again in Asgard a few months later, he had a lovely foal with him. He gave it to Odin. The foal had eight legs and was called Sleipnir. There was no finer horse owned by man or god. Sleipnir's father was Svadilfari and its mother was the white mare. But who do you think the mare *really* was? Remember that one of Loki's other names was Shape Changer.

19

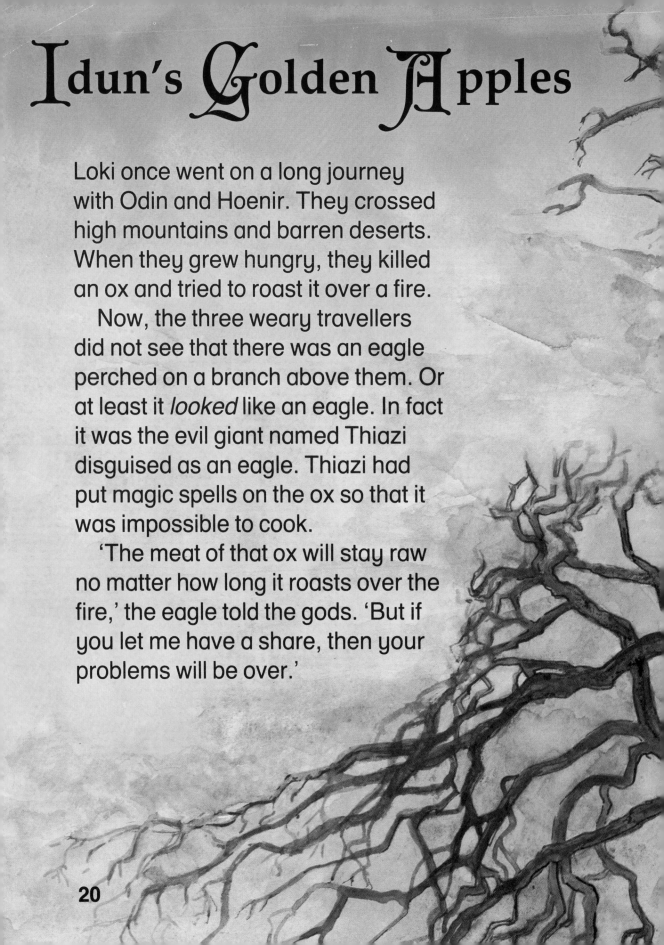

Idun's Golden Apples

Loki once went on a long journey with Odin and Hoenir. They crossed high mountains and barren deserts. When they grew hungry, they killed an ox and tried to roast it over a fire.

Now, the three weary travellers did not see that there was an eagle perched on a branch above them. Or at least it *looked* like an eagle. In fact it was the evil giant named Thiazi disguised as an eagle. Thiazi had put magic spells on the ox so that it was impossible to cook.

'The meat of that ox will stay raw no matter how long it roasts over the fire,' the eagle told the gods. 'But if you let me have a share, then your problems will be over.'

As the gods were getting desperate for food, they decided to give the eagle what he wanted. That was a big mistake! The eagle ate nearly the whole ox.

This made Loki furious. He shouted at the eagle and, picking up a large stick, he shoved it into the eagle's back with all his might.

The eagle shrieked, flapped its wings and flew off into the sky. The stick was still in its back . . . and Loki was still clinging onto the stick!

'Help! Let me go!' begged Loki in terror.

'Only if you promise to bring me the goddess Idun and her apples,' the eagle replied.

Idun's apples were very special. No matter how old the gods were, they became young again when they ate the apples.

'I promise,' cried Loki. So the eagle let him go. Loki then went back to Odin and Hoenir, and together they finished their journey.

Later, Loki sneakily asked Idun to go for a walk with him in the woods outside Asgard. The eagle was waiting there. When he saw them he swooped down, seized both Idun and her apples in his great claws, and carried them off to his home in Giantland.

Without Idun's apples, the gods became older and older. Their hair turned grey and they lost their strength. Their voices became cracked and squeaky. 'What has happened to Idun?' they asked each other. It soon became clear that she had last been seen leaving Asgard with Loki. So the gods captured Loki and threatened to punish him. Loki was terrified. 'I'll bring Idun back — if Freyja will lend me her falcon coat,' he promised.

With the falcon coat, Loki flew to Giantland. Luckily, the eagle had gone off on a sailing trip, so Idun was by herself. Using magic, Loki turned Idun into a nut. Then, holding her tightly, he flew off back to the gods in Asgard.

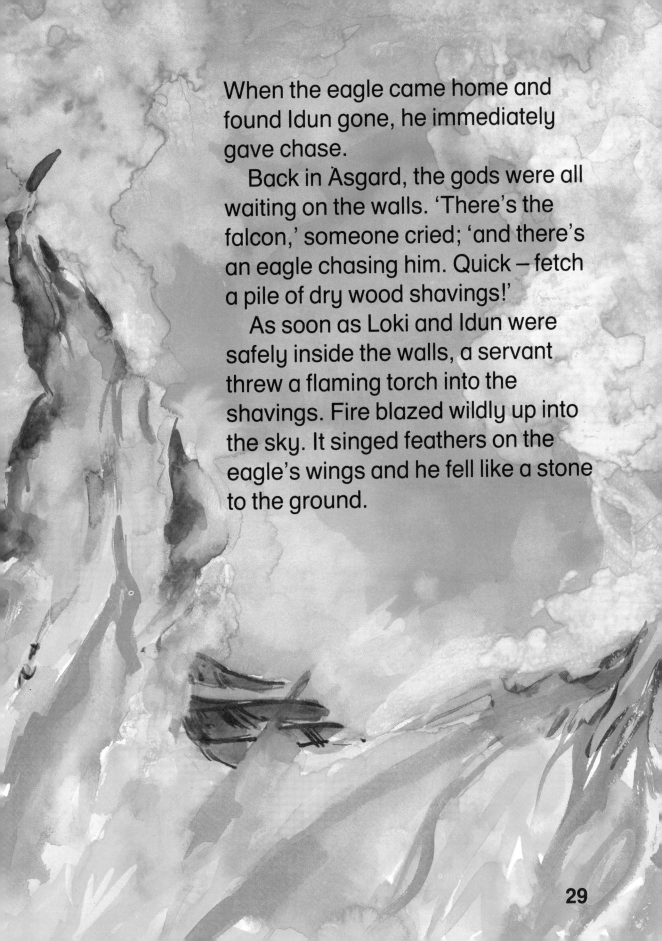

When the eagle came home and found Idun gone, he immediately gave chase.

Back in Asgard, the gods were all waiting on the walls. 'There's the falcon,' someone cried; 'and there's an eagle chasing him. Quick – fetch a pile of dry wood shavings!'

As soon as Loki and Idun were safely inside the walls, a servant threw a flaming torch into the shavings. Fire blazed wildly up into the sky. It singed feathers on the eagle's wings and he fell like a stone to the ground.

The Mead of Poetry

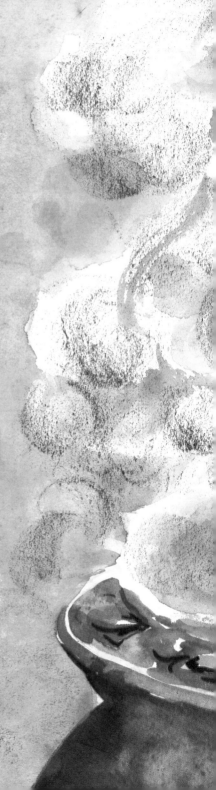

Have you ever wondered how some people are able to make beautiful poetry? Well, this is how:

There was once a man named Kvasir. He was so wise that there was no question to which he did not know the answer. Sadly, Kvasir was murdered by two evil dwarfs. These dwarfs then took Kvasir's blood and brewed a wonderful magic mead with it.

Whoever drank this mead would have the power of words. This means that whatever they said would be strange and beautiful. When other people listened, their hearts would be stirred with deep feelings – and wonderful pictures and ideas would come into their minds. This was the mead of poetry.

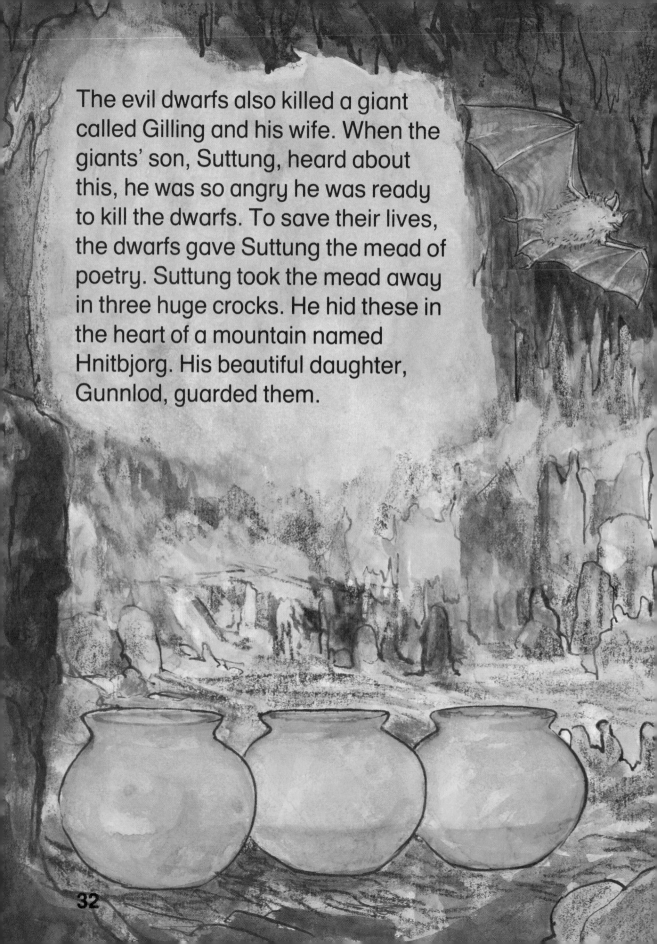

The evil dwarfs also killed a giant called Gilling and his wife. When the giants' son, Suttung, heard about this, he was so angry he was ready to kill the dwarfs. To save their lives, the dwarfs gave Suttung the mead of poetry. Suttung took the mead away in three huge crocks. He hid these in the heart of a mountain named Hnitbjorg. His beautiful daughter, Gunnlod, guarded them.

When the great god Odin heard about the mead of poetry, he said: 'I must get hold of this'. And he worked out a clever plan.

Odin disguised himself as a farmworker. He then went to the farm of Suttung's brother, Baugi. There he found nine workers cutting hay in a field. By trickery, Odin got those nine labourers to cut each other's throats with their scythes.

'Oh dear, how can I finish the harvest with no-one to help me!' cried Baugi when he heard that all his men were dead.

'Don't worry. I can do all the work,' Odin promised him. 'But my wages will be high. You must give me a drink of your brother Suttung's magic mead.'

At first Baugi refused the offer. But later he agreed to help Odin. They got an enormous drill. With this they made a hole into the very heart of the mountain of Hnitbjorg where the mead was hidden. It was a small hole but by changing himself into a snake Odin was able to wriggle down it.

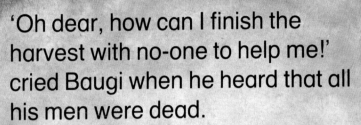

Inside the mountain, Odin met Suttung's daughter, Gunnlod. Gunnlod was lonely and tired of being by herself all the time. She had never seen anyone as handsome as Odin before and so it was not long before Gunnlod fell in love with Odin.

When someone is in love, they will do almost anything to please the other person.

So Gunnlod agreed to let Odin have three sips of her father's magic mead. At the first sip, Odin drank up one whole crock. At the second sip, he drank another whole crock. At the third sip, he drank up all the rest. Then Odin changed himself into an eagle and flew off back to Asgard. But Suttung saw him going. So he changed himself into an eagle too and followed Odin.

The gods put crocks out in the courtyards of Asgard. When Odin flew in, he spat all the mead out of his mouth into these crocks – all except one drop, which fell outside the walls. This one drop is called the poet-taster's share.

'I'm beaten,' Suttung said to himself – and flew off.

Odin gave that magic mead to the gods. But he also gave some to a few men and women. We call these people *poets*. They have wisdom and a knowledge of strange and wonderful things. They also have the power to weave words into beautiful patterns.

Thor's Duel with Hrungnir

Odin once had a horse-race with a giant named Hrungnir. Odin rode his marvellous eight-legged Sleipnir. Hrungnir rode his Gold Mane. Across the sky and over the sea they raced, from horizon to horizon. Before he knew it, Hrungnir found himself inside the walls of Asgard. He was hot – and in a terrible temper because he had lost the race.

The gods invited Hrungnir into the great hall of Valhalla. There they gave him lots of wine to drink. Hrungnir became very drunk. He began to say some very rude things to the gods.

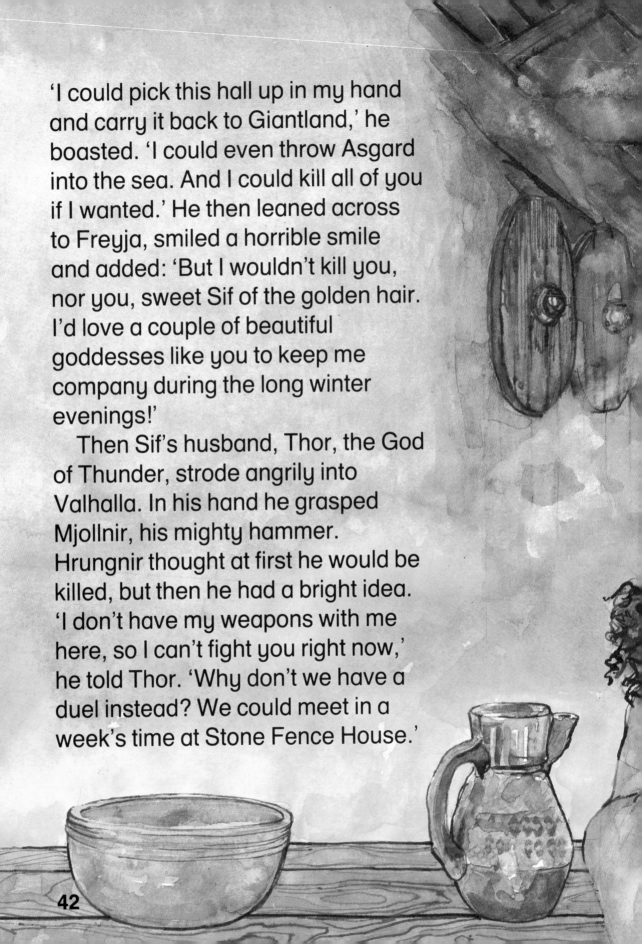

'I could pick this hall up in my hand and carry it back to Giantland,' he boasted. 'I could even throw Asgard into the sea. And I could kill all of you if I wanted.' He then leaned across to Freyja, smiled a horrible smile and added: 'But I wouldn't kill you, nor you, sweet Sif of the golden hair. I'd love a couple of beautiful goddesses like you to keep me company during the long winter evenings!'

Then Sif's husband, Thor, the God of Thunder, strode angrily into Valhalla. In his hand he grasped Mjollnir, his mighty hammer. Hrungnir thought at first he would be killed, but then he had a bright idea. 'I don't have my weapons with me here, so I can't fight you right now,' he told Thor. 'Why don't we have a duel instead? We could meet in a week's time at Stone Fence House.'

Thor had to agree and Hrungnir walked out of Valhalla unharmed.

The giants of Giantland were terrified when they heard about the duel. 'What happens if Hrungnir loses?' they asked each other. 'Thor will kill us all!'

So they made a giant of clay to frighten Thor. They called him Mist Calf and they gave him a horse's heart to make him live. Mist Calf waited with Hrungnir at Stone Fence House for Thor to arrive on the day of the duel. Hrungnir also had his stone shield, and in his hand he carried his favourite weapon – his great whet-stone.

Thor arrived with flashes of lightning and rolls of thunder. Straight away, he hurled his mighty hammer at Hrungnir. Hrungnir replied by hurling his whet-stone at Thor. The two weapons crashed in mid-air and the whet-stone was shattered in two. One splinter buried itself in the ground. The other pierced Thor's head. Injured, the Thunder God crashed to the ground.

But Thor's hammer, Mjollnir, was not broken. It flew through the air and smashed into Hrungnir's skull. The giant was killed instantly. He fell, stone dead, across Thor's body. As for Mist Calf, he was cut down by Thor's servant, Thjalfi.

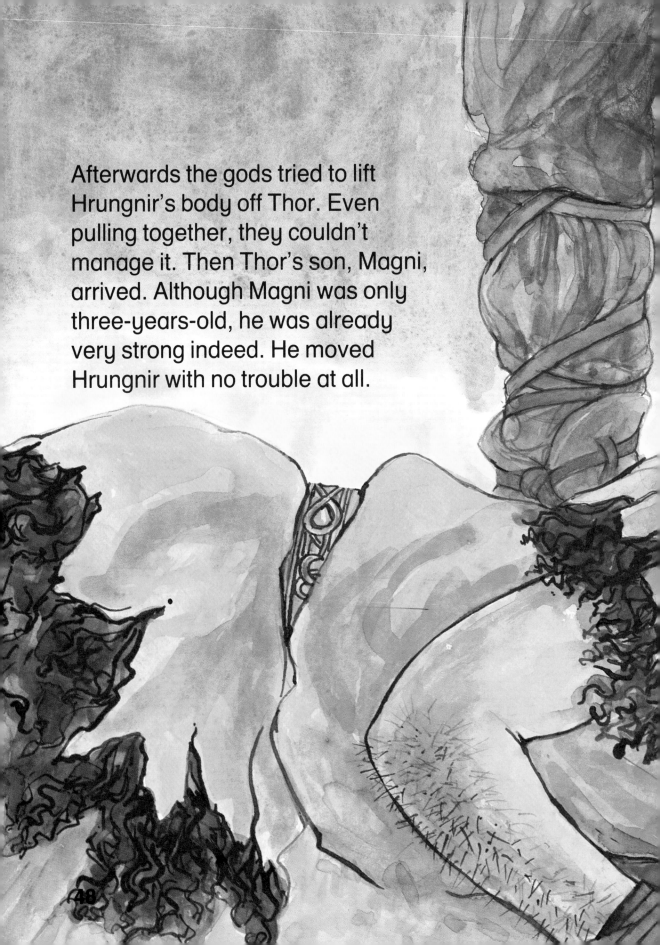

Afterwards the gods tried to lift Hrungnir's body off Thor. Even pulling together, they couldn't manage it. Then Thor's son, Magni, arrived. Although Magni was only three-years-old, he was already very strong indeed. He moved Hrungnir with no trouble at all.

'Thanks, son,' Thor said, sitting up a little shaken but undefeated. 'You should be quite something when you grow up!'

You may be wondering about the stone splinter in Thor's head. Well, that never was pulled out – but it didn't really matter. Thor got better anyway. With gods anything is possible!

The Death of Balder

All the gods and goddesses in Asgard loved Balder because he was kind, wise, brave and handsome. So they were very worried when they heard that he was having bad dreams. Was this perhaps a sign that he was going to die? Fearing it was, Balder's mother, Frigg, made everything in the world promise never to hurt Balder.

Afterwards, the gods tested this out. They struck at Balder with iron and steel. They even threw stones and wooden darts at him, but not a hair of Balder's head was harmed. Then the gods laughed and began to throw things at Balder for fun.

Sly Loki hated Balder and longed to do him harm. He found out that the mistletoe had not made any promises about Balder. Loki took a twig of mistletoe and gave it to the blind god Hod. 'Throw it at Balder' Loki told Hod. 'It can't hurt him.'

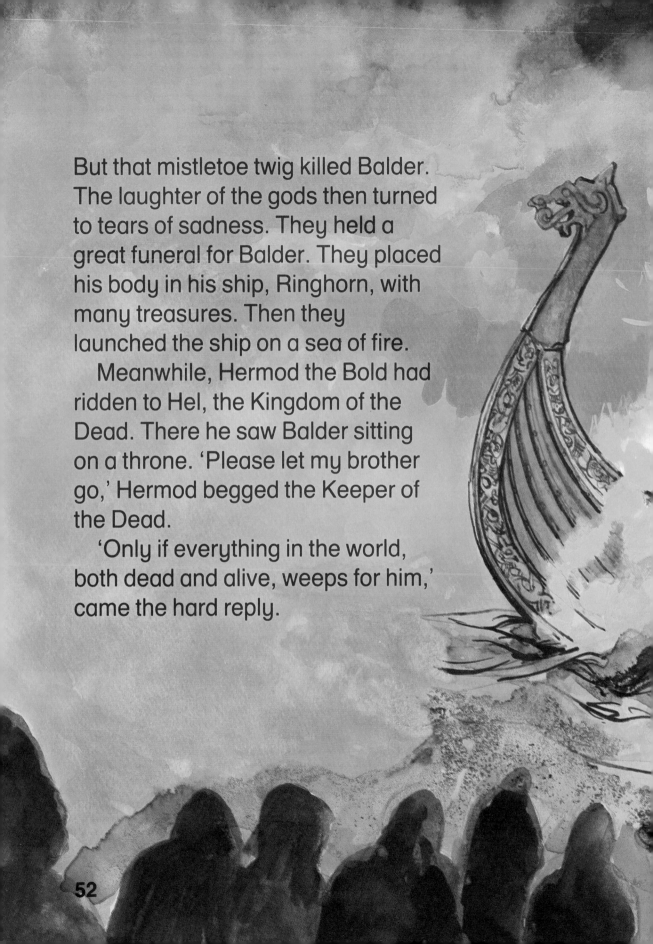

But that mistletoe twig killed Balder. The laughter of the gods then turned to tears of sadness. They held a great funeral for Balder. They placed his body in his ship, Ringhorn, with many treasures. Then they launched the ship on a sea of fire.

Meanwhile, Hermod the Bold had ridden to Hel, the Kingdom of the Dead. There he saw Balder sitting on a throne. 'Please let my brother go,' Hermod begged the Keeper of the Dead.

'Only if everything in the world, both dead and alive, weeps for him,' came the hard reply.

The gods sent messengers throughout the whole world. Their message was: *Please weep for Balder*. Everywhere the answer was a glad *Yes*, except in one dark cave. 'Let Hel hold what it has!' screamed the evil giantess Thokk.

Who could have been so cruel and evil? Only one person. Remember, one of Loki's other names was Shape Changer . . .

When the gods saw that Loki was the cause of all this trouble, they became very angry indeed. 'He shall pay the price!' they declared.

In great fear, Loki ran and hid on a mountain. He built a tower so that he could see in every direction. He sometimes changed himself into a salmon in order to hide in rivers.

But the gods caught Loki in their nets. They threw him into a deep cave and bound him to three great stones. Over his head they fastened a snake. Loki's wife, Sigyn, held out a basin to catch the poison that dripped from the snake's fangs. But every now and then she had to go away to empty the basin. Then the poison fell onto Loki's face. *Ugh!*

Loki will stay like that until *Ragnarok* (the end of the world). At that time, the weather will turn dreadfully cold. Battles will break out everywhere and millions of people will be killed. The sun and the moon will be eaten by wolves. The stars will go out, the earth will quake and mountains will topple. The sea will seethe with poison and the sky will be torn down.

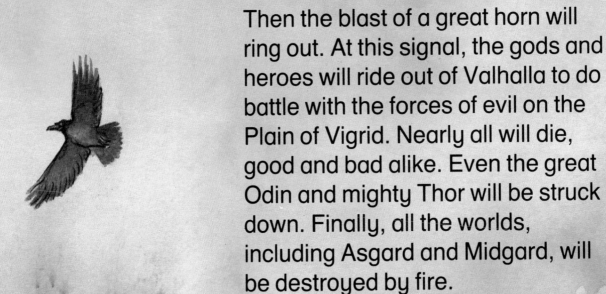

Then the blast of a great horn will ring out. At this signal, the gods and heroes will ride out of Valhalla to do battle with the forces of evil on the Plain of Vigrid. Nearly all will die, good and bad alike. Even the great Odin and mighty Thor will be struck down. Finally, all the worlds, including Asgard and Midgard, will be destroyed by fire.

Later, much later, a new earth, fresh and green, will rise out of a blue sea. Then a new race of gods and men will appear. Life will start all over again. Always remember that every end is a new beginning.